CW00811124

Svengali

EVE NICOL

Nicol McNichol
GLASGOW

First paperback edition 2022

Nicol McNichol, Glasgow

Copyright © Eve Nicol, 2022

All rights strictly reserved. Application for permission for any use, professional or amateur, should be made in advance, prior to any proposed use via contact details on
www.evenicol.com

No performance may be given unless a licence has been obtained.

No part of this book may be reproduced or used in any manner without the prior written permission of the copyright owner.

ISBN 978-1-3999-2874-8

Printed and bound by CPI Group (UK) Ltd, Croydon, CR0 4YY

Eve Nicol in association with Pleasance and Pitlochry
Festival Theatre present

SVENGALI

by Eve Nicol

Pleasance Courtyard, Edinburgh

5 – 28 August 2022

Svengali

by Eve Nicol

CAST

Svengali   **Chloe-Ann Tylor**

Director   **Eve Nicol**
Movement Director   **Robbie Gordon**

.

CHLOE-ANN TYLOR – The Svengali

Chloe-Ann graduated from the Royal Conservatoire of Scotland in 2016.

Her theatre credits include, *I Am Tiger (*Imaginate & Horsecross Arts / Perth Theatre), *Doppler* (Grid Iron) *Mrs Puntila and Her Man Matti* (Royal Lyceum Edinburgh & Citizens Theatre in association with DOT Theatre, Istanbul), *The Stornoway Way* (Dogstar Theatre Company), *Close Quarters* (Out of Joint / Sheffield Crucible*), Hansel and Gretel*, *Trainspotting* (Citizens Theatre), *The Merchant of Venice* (Bard in the Botanics), *Titus Andronicus* (Dundee Rep).

EVE NICOL - Writer & Director

Eve is a Glaswegian playwright and director.

As Writer; *Robin Hood* (Cumbernauld Theatre) *If You're Feeling Sinister [a play with songs]* (BBC Arts and Avalon in association with Tron), *One Life Stand* (Middle Child), *First Woman* (Traverse Theatre) and *A Brownie Guide to Aviation* (Slung Low & Unicorn Theatre).

As Director; *I Can Go Anywhere* (Traverse Theatre), *The Drift (*National Theatre of Scotland), *The Mistress Contract* (Tron Theatre Company), *Exquisite Corpse*, *We Interrupt This Programme* (Glasgow Lunchtime Theatre), *The Undiscovered Creature*, *Sea Wall* and *The Pitchfork Disney* (Heroes Theatre).

As Associate Director; *THEM!* (National Theatre of Scotland), *What Girls Are Made Of* (Raw Material & Traverse Theatre). As Assistant Director; *Local Hero*, *The Hour We Knew Nothing of Each Other* and *Glory On Earth* (Royal Lyceum Theatre), *Cock* (Tron Theatre).
www.evenicol.com

ROBBIE GORDON – Movement Director

Robbie Gordon is a theatre-maker born in Prestonpans specialising in making work with and for communities. He trained at the Royal Conservatoire of Scotland, graduating in 2016 with the Drama in Education Award.

He is the co-founder of the critically acclaimed "fiercely curious" (The Herald) Wonder Fools, Creative Engagement Director at the Gaiety Theatre and Creative Development Producer for the Traverse Theatre.

Robbie is the co-creator of Positive Stories for Negative Times, an international participatory project by Wonder Fools in association with the Traverse Theatre, which has engaged over 7,000 young people in 16 different countries.

Selected credits include, Writer and Movement Director of *549: Scots of the Spanish Civil War* (Wonder Fools in association with the Citizens Theatre); Writer and Movement Director of *The Coolidge Effect* (Wonder Fools); Writer and Director of *McNeill of Tranent: Fastest Man in the World* (Wonder Fools); Writer of *When the Sun Meets The Sky* (Traverse Theatre and Capital Theatres); Movement Director of *The Enemy* (National Theatre of Scotland); Associate Director of *Square Go* (Francesca Moody Productions); Lead Artist (Ayrshire) on Danny Boyle's *Pages of the Sea* (National Theatre of Scotland); Creator of *Open Your Lugs* (Ayr Gaiety); Producer and Director of Class Act (Traverse Theatre).
www.robbiegordon.org

PLEASANCE THEATRE TRUST

The Pleasance Theatre Trust aims to create a compelling platform to discover, nurture and support fresh artistic talent from across the globe. As a not-for-profit organisation, all proceeds from the Festival and our London base are invested back into the development of new people and new ideas.
Since opening in 1985, the Pleasance has become renowned for delivering an inspiring programme year on year that uniquely embodies the spirit of the Festival Fringe.

Pleasance Futures is the artist development strand of The Pleasance, acting as an incubator for bold new theatre-makers to make their mark. Pleasance Futures is committed to discovering and supporting the most exciting new theatrical voices, nurturing the development of emerging companies, young performers and new writers.

www.pleasance.co.uk/futures

PITLOCHRY FESTIVAL THEATRE

For over 70 years, Pitlochry Festival Theatre has been Highland Perthshire's artistic heart and soul, attracting over 100,000 visitors each year.

PFT is famous for producing plays and musicals that delight theatregoers of all ages. International-standard performances featuring award-winning artists, writers and directors and outstanding set and costume designs combine to bring audiences to their feet.

www.pitlochryfestivaltheatre.com

A WORD FROM WRITER & DIRECTOR
EVE NICOL

'TRILBY' BY GEORGE DU MAURIER

Svengali is a fast and loose adaptation of *Trilby*, a hugely popular Victorian novel. It was a blockbuster. "Trilbymania" swept the land. It's largely forgotten today, but the cultural impact remains. The story directly influenced *Dracula* and *Phantom of the Opera*. It's from the costume of Trilby in the stage adaptation that the "trilby hat" got its name.

George du Maurier's book tells the story of three clean-cut young British artists and their adventures in bohemian Paris. However, the sensational B-plot of artists' model Trilby and the sinister Svengali captured the audience's imagination.

Svengali, an influential and talented musician, takes the tone-deaf Trilby under his wing. With his teaching, she becomes a singing sensation. Trilby and Svengali change their humble fortunes, selling out opera houses across Europe. But Trilby can only sing whilst making direct eye contact with her hypnotic mentor. When he dies unexpectedly in the middle of a concert, the suddenly awakened but disorientated Trilby has no control over her prior abilities and rapidly declines. Trilby catches sight of a portrait of her maestro. She is mesmerised by his painted eyes and dies whispering his name. Talk about melodrama!

Du Maurier writes Svengali as the Victorian, archetypical "exotic Jew". The outdated cultural depictions of "Jewishness" are heightened by the sketches du Maurier accompanied his work. Our *Svengali* wants to leave these harmful, antisemitic tropes in the Victorian era. The character has transcended his source material to become the dictionary definition of manipulative control. The name of Svengali has been used to describe figures including the Spice Girls' manager Simon Fuller, political puppet master Dominic Cummings, and football boss Sven-Goran Eriksson

This *Svengali* resurrects the seductive 19th-century villain and repositions him as polarising figure for the #MeToo era. *Svengali* pulls back the curtain on the complicated dynamic between a mentor and protege.

SVENGALI & ME

In the twenty years I've been involved in professional theatre, I have been placed in the hands of eight male, middle-aged mentors. In 2018, #MeToo conversations made me re-examine my varied relationships with my mentors and the dynamics at work. The ferocious reckoning with power, desire and gender mangled my brain. I am confused, angry, and ashamed of some of the things I had "let happen" or happened to me. Yet also hugely protective of the men who offered their time and knowledge for my development.

My relationships with my mentors have been frustrating, insightful, heartbreaking, fun, explorative, exploitative but overall - good. I get validation and access to their professional world. But what do they get from having a young, over-eager woman traipsing around after them? *Svengali* is my examination of this question.

GENDER FUCKERY

The central conceit of *Svengali* is that it is the story of a middle-aged man's experience told through the voice and body of a young woman. It is an act of transference and possession where we see the "villain" through the sympathetic eyes of a young woman. It's a "one man show" performed by an actress. The script provides an opportunity to play with gender and sexuality in a non-literal way.

For our production, the men who inspired us included David Bowie in his 1984 Serious Moonlight tour, judge Patrick Grant from BBC's *Sewing Bee,* Andrew Lincoln from Channel 4's *Teachers*, Bryan Ferry, Paul McKenna, the vampires from 1983's *The Hunger* and the ultimate physiologically driven tennis coach, Patrick Mouratoglou.

'

SVENGALI

Eve Nicol

NOTE ON THE TEXT

This play centres on a middle-aged male character. It should be performed by a young, female actor.

The game comes in conjuring up this older male character through tone, expression, and subtitles of body language.

Talc in hair, John Wayne swaggers and fake moustaches – AVOID AT ALL COSTS! It should be sexy in its ambiguity.

Only when the illusion is clearly established, do occasional shades of the reality of the young, female actor in front of us comes through.

By the end of the play, the younger, feminine energy has broken through completely.

We end with a young, female character talking directly to us, simply and unadorned.

'I used to try and do all I could - be a daughter to him, as I couldn't be anything else.'

-   Trilby

'And, ach! what a beautiful skeleton you will make!'
-   Svengali

Trilby by George du Maurier.

CHARACTERS

Svengali

This text went to print before the end of rehearsals and so may differ slightly from the play as performed.

'Bela Lugosi's Dead' by Bauhaus.

A saturated blue light.

SVENGALI. Their bare feet stick out the bottom of an impeccable cuffed tan suit. Their eyes are impenetrable behind glossy reflective sunglasses.

SVENGALI takes a tennis ball from their pocket and bounces it rhythmically against the ground. Thump, catch, thump, catch, thump, catch. The hypnotic rhythm pulls the dark in round us. They bounce the ball throughout the following.

SVENGALI

What separates a champion from the swarm is all up here.

A forefinger to the forehead.

It's a mental game. To become a champion, you need discipline. To become a champion, you need the support to push your limits. To become a master – requires a little bit of magic.

It started for me when mum brought home a telly. Summer becomes about Wimbledon.

Arthur Ashe is punching the air. Cameras perve on girls flagging down Bjorn with their knickers in Borgasmic rapture. Billie Jean King breaks records, and Linda Seigel breaks out of her halter neck! Bursting out of her dress and into my dreams. "Thanks for the mammaries!"

I splurge my lunch money on a Woolies racket. Devote days to the shattered glass and anthills of the council court. I elbowed my way into the Junior circuit. The number of children I made cry with my backhand.

But I never went further.

The mini-McEnroe in my head defeated me. You know the little voice? He's a superbrat who punishes my every slip-up. You cannot be serious! *(warningly)* Ho. You don't have the guts, you looser, you chicken. Superbrat stopped me from getting further than stepping into my old coach's shoes after they hung up their Stan Smiths.

That was until Trilby happened.

Everyone at the club is irritable in the gloomy June heat. Clouds sit oppressively low. My headache that won't shift. I'm the top club pro at a lovely facility by now. I know I'm the top because I am paid the most and work the least. I am working with a young woman. For the sake of argument, I'll call her Subject X. Subject X plays a fine game. Bit bull-headed, however. Doesn't listen. I am getting to a point there's little left I can accomplish with her.

I am deathly bored.

WHOOSH!

A typhoon of fur flies onto the court.

A dog! Dragging a lead behind it.

The dog barks, loud as it is fast, piercing holes in our balls with its needle teeth. Subject X sprints from it, but the dog thinks – "oh goody! A game!". This teddy-bear-with-fangs looking thing nipping at her bobby socks. They're looping the net. Benny Hill would be proud.

The duty manager comes out of the pavilion. His shoulders stiffen at the chaos on my court. I need to take control.

My racket swings up and - I'm not particularly kind to the rascal.

Then something even more ferocious than the four-legged dervish rattles the fence. Trilby. A young woman, face hideous with screaming. "Get your hands off. You monster!"

I point Subject X towards the showers. Stuff the hairball into my kit bag. I'm followed to the car park with this girl beating at my shoulders. I bundle the dog and the girl in the boot of my Volvo. I drive to the vet. The posh one where Alice got the cat declawed. The dog only needs a couple of stitches and the humiliation of a satellite dish.

It will survive.

Trilby calms down when she realises I've barely issued the dog a spanking and not brained it.

She's better company as I give her a lift into town.

The pup keeps silent in the back of the car. She dog-sits to earn pocket money; it will be weeks until the owner is home. She is curious about what I do. I tell her.

I'm creating the greatest tennis star the world has ever seen.

I typically receive a smirk in response when I say this.

But Trilby seems interested.

I am developing a theory that man is limitless if we can subdue the negative ego in our heads.

Oh god, you're going on. My negative ego rears its head. Come on, man. What the hell is wrong with you, you fuckup?

Gnasher snoring happily. 'Smooth Classics' on the radio. Me trying to impress this young woman with my ideas. I shut up.

As we drive, she relaxes her arm on the cupholder.

The sleeves of her cropped denim jacket rolled up in the heat. Her forearms shine. The hair on them - tawny and thick but not unattractive. I can't see the triceps, but from the glint of the wrist and her grip on the armrest, I see a championship arm.

I inform her so.

She strikes a strongman pose, straining against the seatbelt.

She's funny.

I enjoy funny women.

I go home, devour two helpings of spaghetti carbonara and have sex with Alice for the first time in a year. Alice brings me coffee in the morning, and I tell her I worship her.

Surprise! Trilby rattles the fence, waving a punnet of strawberries. An apology for the swearing and battery. As if I'm not the one who brained Scrappy-Doo. And not just strawberries! Cream! The squirty kind! I'm almost embarrassed to eat something so cliche.

We sit in the pavilion shade. Trilby piles the out-of-season fruit with sugar and air. She kicks off her sandals, digging her feet into the coolness of the clipped grass. An ant runs over her toes. I ache to lean over and stroke it off.

She talks. She spills everything. Exposing herself seems to come easy. Her ponytail canters along with her as she chatters about her life. Picking up jobs here and there – dog walking, house sitting. Saving up for a life by the sea. She was an artists' model. Loved standing around with an excuse to zone out. It was brilliant. Easy money, spent on school books for her younger brother. Her favourite pose? Athenea. Armour-bound, bursting from the head of Zeus.

The life of a muse was idyllic until a flirtation with a painter went sour. What had started as liberating and freewheeling became possessive and puritan once they'd fallen into bed. He became ashamed of her nakedness and caused a scene in the studio. Her bookings had dried up whilst he is exhibited at RSA.

I gobble up each slight shift in her features, riding the wave of her expressiveness.

Is she like this with everyone?

I'm caught out when she turns directly to me and asks -

"Greatest tennis player in the world then?"

Yup.

I feel a stupid pride to hear my words repeated from Trilby's mouth.

"How will you do it?"

I understand the game as no one else understands it. Or ever will.

"Go on."

Tennis is a game you play against yourself. What I do, what I want to do, is break down the internal ego at play. Free the body. Is it possible to be consciously unconscious? Push someone to play out of their mind? Can I compel someone to a state so concentrated, focused, and still that the body works without interference from thoughts?

"An empty head!"

I suppose so.

"Wow, that sounds divine. Do they have to be any good?"

Here comes the genius of my ideas. Anyone can reach peak performance. If only they have an open mind.

"Fancy yourself as a Henry Higgins?"

I'm surprised by the reference.

More of a Svengali.

I'm getting into this, twisting the heads from daisies as I speak.

All animals fall under a spell. There are powers to exploit. Turn a rabbit on its back. Clutch a chicken's head to the ground. Tickle a trout. You drive home and can't recollect anything of the journey. On autopilot, the ego doesn't receive any fuel. The voices in our heads quiet. We exist as unburdened beings. Truly liberated from mediocrity.

The skill in the coach comes from finding the right trigger.

Everyone is different. Find the right trigger and unleash the
potential within the human body.

The hypnosis spell unlocks sensational, untapped states in us.
Shuts down everything else except the bare minimum it takes
to survive. Unbothered by thoughts of food, shelter, sex –

Strawberry juice drips down her wrist. Being alone with her
feels illicit.

She says she'll think about it. Becoming the greatest tennis
player in the world.

I hadn't realised I made the invitation.

It's impossible not to look at her arse as she disappears round
the corner. You're an asshole, Superbrat pipes up.

Gnasher becomes a regular, tied up by the club gates whilst
Trilby visits. The deeper I go with Trilby — with her
roughness, lack of coordination, and coarseness — the less
interested I am in Subject X.

I spot one million things with Trilby that I can affect. She has
the makings of a champion. The physical strength, yes. But
this isn't rugby I'm talking about. Tennis is about style, flair,
and a pleasing face. We like our whites white, and Trilby is a
great-looking girl, a fantastic-looking girl. The kind of girl on
the front of Pepsi bottles.

But above all, she is of a sympathetic mind.

Hungry for instruction.

I frustrate Subject X.

I'm not as present as I used to be. I have a decision to
determine.

Two girls.

Trilby or Subject X.

One of me.

I get them to play a tiebreaker. I'm deciding which one of
these girls secures my time. The drama gives me a thrill.

Trilby keeps her eyes on me. She serves with too little power.
Every shot falls foul of the court.

Fault.

Fault.

Fault.

Subject X delivers a beautiful ace that is impossible for Trilby
to return. The girls shake hands.

But it had to be Trilby.

Subject X is - I don't know what Subject X's doing now. Wait,
yes, I do. Subject X's working in a bar. Correct choice made,
yes? Obviously. Subject X didn't accomplish anything with her
talent.

We formalise our relationship. I am Trilby's coach. She, my
student. A team.

There's something that I want to try. It's essential I have
Trilby's buy-in.

I instruct her to sit on the bench.

I sit opposite.

Look at me. Into the whites of my eyes.

She avoids my gaze because of something from our caveman past.

Look at me.

I run my finger round the palm of her hand. Pass across her wrists and forearms. Soon her eyes close, and her face relaxes.

Her breathing slows. Skin chills. A gentle hum is assuring me she's still with me. Running like a fridge. Completely ambient.

I've got her.

In my first possession of her, three decades of tension roll off my shoulders.

Is she asleep?

Then open your eyes and look at me.

She is spellbound.

I set her up with serve after serve. She moves swiftly. Her body, freed from thought, naturally responds. Balls crack against her racket. A colossal power emanates from her with ease. Good girl.

We decompress in our spot behind the pavilion.

She chugs an entire bottle of water. Her eyes are saucer huge. Tongue thick, stumbling over sentences. She's all - God, the strength of her body. Where did that come from? Did I see her catch that lob? Yeah, I saw it. Did you have fun. "I enjoyed making you happy"

She's got her whole head stuck under the water fountain, laping it up. She grins - she's in.

> *They are enthusiastic and energetic. Giddy. If there was music, it's be Iggy Pop's 'Funtime'.*

Before I can really teach her anything, I must unteach her everything she knows.

Her breathing, her posture – everything is wrong. She doesn't know how uncoordinated she is. I heap on compliments of her grace and witness it become true.

I move on to her diet. I save her from cans of Monster and Lunchables. I split portions of Alice's tuna steaks and potato salads under the courtside umbrellas.

Everybody at the club loves her. In one year, she becomes more part of the fabric of this place than I have in ten. She knows the name of the woman who hands out the towels. The hipster that always messes up my order in the cafe smiles now. The little girls who swarm the place before and after school worship her without Trilby having to do anything. They can't name it yet, but they already recognise the power Trilby possesses. They gather round her ankles. I set them to work collecting Trilby's loose balls at the end of our sessions.

My role is to observe her results in a detached manner. Her body will learn.

We run suicides side by side. I do all the conditioning with Trilby. I want her to know I'm beside her.

Because she's blindfolded, didn't I say? It's for its own safety that you hood a hawk. Close its focus. Gain its trust.

Under hypnosis, we bind her hands to the racket. Looks a bit like a sealion, but it is effective.

Her body is mottled as a river stone with bruises. Perfect circles all over her legs and arms.

She delights in the proof of her efforts. She jabs them with a chopstick as we eat dinner off our laps and laughs.

How can she keep laughing?

Maybe she's simple.

Maybe she's laughing at me?

"I'd put my hand under your boot if you asked me to."

I don't ask her. I don't test her. These kinds of provocations trouble me. Plunging me into deep jungles of fear.

I'm not a sadist. Nothing makes me harder than getting someone to smile. Learn tricks to amuse. You reckon Trilby is a hot shot – watch this.

They juggle a set of tennis balls.

Impressive eh. Have you ever seen Andy Murray do that? The girls love it.

Before we can reach the big tournaments, we need funding.

Trilby drags me along to club events and fundraising things, which I hate, but she soars at.

We're both out of place amongst people who never worry about heating bills. But they've adopted her.

She says she wants me here, merely having me in the corner, grumpy and nursing my orange juice as I am. That makes my balls feel as big as space hoppers.

It's fun to sidle up to her and brush my thumb in her palm. Watch her shiver and shake. Smiles as she tries to maintain a conversation as the spell comes over her.

We get a spot in the US Open.

It's her first time on a plane. I run my hands over her palms to soothe her as we take off. She's a wildcard entry - and a sensation from the first serve.

Once people have time to gasp and nudge their neighbour about this breakout wonder, this revelation of human ability - a colossal roar fills the court.

I coast on the ecstatic delight of the crowd. Trilby is machine fierce. Her opponent furrows trenches in the court, their legs cartwheeling to keep up with her. The tension in the stands tightens like an elastic band with each hit. She keeps up a remarkable volley against the front runner. My heart beating with the pock-pock-pock of the ball. The hush is as oppressive and impressive as the tight grip on the heart that happens when the fistful of earth drops on the coffin.

Out!

The madness from the stands is immediate. Trilby steeps in the adoration, smiling and waving at me as I join the cheering in the stands.

Good girl.

She was a fox at the side of the road. How many people drove past, taking her for dead, before I stopped to look? To think I made that success causes my thumbs to itch with electricity.

She's playing for the world now. Cameras dash to keep up with her as she blazes through the tournament. Match after match, she dominates. Evidence that our way of working – works. People ditch their favourites to come watch my little wonder.

It's her first major title.

They hum a lullaby, 'Lavender's Blue'.

We reunite with churchlike calm in the darkened locker room.

Exhausted, her face a war of red and white. I hold a cool towel to her brow and speak softly to her. Good girl, well done.

I bend down and take off this angel's shoes. Her eyes flutter in her head – she might go anytime. I speak to her, and she clings to my voice for long enough to make our escape.

She sleeps in the car to the hotel. Head against my shoulder.

I carry her up to the room, hands cupping the back of her legs. Warm. Slightly sticky.

I cocoon her in a blanket. Housekeeping left chocolate on the pillows. I press a corner of the sweetness between her lips. She needs to eat.

I stroke her hair.

There's a crowd of press and fans below, speculating. I shut the blinds.

The Australian Open!

A spider. Huntsman, is it? Huge as my hand. Hairy bastard.

This guy crawls its way onto Trilby's chest mid point. All hairy digits brushing up against her throat. She doesn't blink.

But the scene! Chaos! The umpire falls faint from their chair. The stands froth with regurgitated Fosters. But my marvellous Trilby isn't fazed. She takes out the hometown hero with an impressive drop shot. The sports pages followed with the headline, "Curse of the Spider Woman." I keep our clippings until the binders outgrow our checked baggage. They burst from the folders and flutter behind us through departures.

The hypnosis gives her more energy than I can control.

We wrestle.

On the odd occasion she lets me win.

She steps onto the Paris clay with a black eye.

I monitor her from the stands with two.

In these fights, she's fierce and batters me like she means it. Screaming and spitting in my face. I'll haul her down the hall and hurl her into her locker until she's silent. When I allow her out, and she'll be kitten soft and pliable. I'll pluck her up by the braid and get a whack across the face in reply.

I'll struggle on top of her and strap her down with her own shoelaces. I'll have my hands at my belt to thrash her - a fistful of leather - when that laugh starts up. Wiggling and grinning and breathing heavily. Her face prawn pink and shining.

She pants. "Free me and we'll go again."

It is good. It is. It is good. Good. Honest. A good thing.

These battles.

It's good.

It's so much better that I allow myself to be her punching bag, to let Trilby exorcise her demons through me. Prevent her from turning on herself with a constant usurping Superbrat of her own.

And I think I'm overdue a battering. I deserve it. I deserve the slap on my face and the "Try me, you fucker."

We celebrate the French win, with a battle for the ages. She's bust her lip, and we're at the hospital, evading everybody's eyes and holding hands under the paper sheets.

Whilst she's being stitched up, I wander the corridors. No one stops me. The nurses smile. Ply me with patisserie and cheek kisses. Cancer patients shake my hand for a job well done. "Bravo, bravo, monsieur". I take a photo with *le concierge*.

There are only two weeks between Paris and Wimbledon. Rather than resting, I increase the intensity of training. We'll be in front of a home crowd.

An award ceremony is a distraction, but Trilby knows the importance of making an appearance. Smile, shake hands, suck up to a sponsor or six.

We've been inundated with offers to dress her for the shindig. I lay out our options in the hotel suite. Dress her up in diamonds, furs, velvet, and lace. Her radiance has me in tears at her feet.

This is a big bucks do. My glass of champagne is never less than half full. Trilby does the rounds of the swanky ballroom. I follow behind like a bridesmaid. She's the main attraction. None of us here would be surprised if she grew wings and joined the painted muses who look down from the domed ceiling. My heart is in the heavens with them. Tense with having to share her. If the courts are my natural habitat – this is hers. A room stuffed with minor royals and GQ Men of the Year to impress.

She drifts further and further from me. Deeper into the crowd of expensive suits. I elbow my way back to her side. Try to get her attention with a stroke of palm. She bats me away. Makes me hold her drink as she steps on stage to collect her prize.

I raise a toast to her with the rest of the room. The champagne is sour.

I take myself outside and smoke with the rest of the losers. Punish her with my absence. My mind swims with all the reasons I idolise and despise her.

Superbrat comes for me in the quiet of my hotel room. Hotshot in a cheap suit. Pawing at her like a dog. God, get us back to fields and gyms where I have some control.

The door rattles.

She's come for me.

It's late.

She wants in.

Blood beats in my ears. I could open the door. Slip her inside. Scoop warm water from the shower over her. Peel dress off. Tuck her into bed. I could join her.

I'm cornered, quivering over what her body might reduce me to.

She doesn't need to come here just to please me.

"I'm here to please myself."

You don't know what you're asking for.

"I do. A bruise, a break and a quiet head."

I could annihilate her. Haul her onto my shoulder like stolen plunder. Quarter her and display her head on the hotel veranda. I could devour her from the neck down. I could floss her meat from my teeth with handfuls of her hair.

Chain on, give her an inch. Eye to eye.

If we start this, I don't know if I can stop.

"I'm strong."

It isn't strength. It's self-harm. It's monstrous.

"Monstrous has won us three titles in our first proper season."

It has.

"Not luck, or talent. It's been sacrifice."

I know.

"I've done everything you've asked."

I know, I know. You've been so good.

She wallops the door. Shudders on its hinges. People are going to come and see the commotion.

Let's not spoil it. Hammering an old cunt's door in the middle of the night. I don't want you.

Her voice is low and dangerous.

"I know your secrets."

Her power makes me open the door.

Trilby eyes glow. She's won. She runs her finger in my hand. Crosses over wrists and forearms. I shake at her touch. I am not brave enough for this.

"Look at me."

I run.

She howls after me through hotel corridors that look like the Titanic.

I flag down a taxi in my bare feet. Escape Trilby and the tuxedoed herds. Where are you going, fuck up? Somewhere safe. Two hours later and still shaking, I creep in next to Alice. My chest is tight as I pretend to sleep. Alice rolls away. "You stink."

I have the gall of returning to the marital abode whilst the McClusky's have their annual barbecue next door. Alice banishes me to the basement. She wants all trace of me gone.

I'm bent over. The native creepy crawlies pay no attention to me as I try to discern what's worth salvaging. Things have squashed over thirty years, and getting them out is harder than it was putting them in.

Above me, ice rattles against glass. Here's Janet McClusky with a jug of homemade lemonade, wanting a proper look at the monster before I'm banished forever.

Impatient to leave, I yank something that doesn't want to be yanked and fall. Boxes of a life tumble down on top of me. I can't move. Alice screams at me to stay still. I'm not going anywhere, Alice. Janet's dropped her pitcher in shock. Lemonade runs down the grooves of my peace offering aged oak parquet floor and splashes onto my face. The drip drip drip of Chinese lemonade torture. The extended McClusky clan comes see the show. It is a delight to escape the shame by passing out.

I'm imprisoned for a fortnight. I miss all the Wimbledon prep. The hospital is terribly concerned and don't want to discharge me yet.

Trilby doesn't come to me.

I go on a hunger strike. Snarl at the nurses. Make myself as unpleasant as possible. The crueller I am, the more they regard it as a challenge to tame me. Kill me with their kindness. One fluffs my pillow, "Your girl is on the telly." I bark at her to turn it off. She leaves the room with the remote.

So there she is.

Trilby, looking like butter wouldn't melt. I didn't authorise this interview. She speaks to someone off-camera.

She has had some time to think.

She is retiring from tennis once the season is over.

She has her own dreams to chase.

She's twenty-five.

At the top.

She's quitting.

People won't understand, but she's okay with that. She is so grateful for everything tennis has given her. Tennis has given her freedom and experiences. But. It was never her dream. She is spent. She has nothing left to offer. She has given absolutely everything she has to tennis.

"I will always love tennis."

She embraces the interviewer. Her eyes dart down the lens and wring my heart.

Bitch.

I made a mistake. I chose the wrong girl.

Poured all my skill, pity and charity into this an ungrateful insect.

She's left none for me.

I commandeer a phone. Don't want to let her off lightly. Tell her what I think of her stunt. Throwing it all away over pride. Ten, fifty over a hundred calls that day. Unanswered.

I'm discharged to my new place. A bungalow on the skirts of the infested courts I grew up by. A bed, a TV and not much

else. I stay inside with the curtains shut. Sunshine gives me
headaches. Smoke. days away. Watching her in the
tournament. Casual and cool without me.

It's midnight. I'm asleep in front of the highlights programme.
My phone rings. She's back.

She's spinning and breathless, and cool it, girl, breathe. What's
wrong?

Her younger brother is dead.

She spoiled her family and childhood pals with her unwanted
prize money. All gone off on a dream holiday in Corfu.
Straight out the plane, he jumped on a moped and launched
himself off a cliff. She's fractured with guilt.

Breathe. Clear head. Your body knows what to do. It can get
through this.

I hear her sisters in the background. "Who are you talking to?"
"No one."

I keep the line open. I coach her through the funeral from the
end of the phone. She needed to be catatonic until the coffin
was in the ground, her head thick with sorrow.

I was never confident her brother was, in fact, her brother.
Too many years between them and too many similarities
shared. Her grief is too big.

What about the tournament? I can be with her at centre court.
Come on, the last bastion to our grand slam? We should see
this one through together.

"No. I shouldn't have called. It's done."

The line goes dead.

She doesn't - that's not. This isn't what was agreed. I am the coach. She the student. I command. She obeys. She doesn't control me.

I still have strings I can pull. I blag a spectator ticket to centre court. It's a festival atmosphere around the poison green grass. High spec cameras, overpriced strawberries and perky, polished people press in around me. Desperate to see her. Keep hat pulled low. Sunglass on.

I can tell she feels my presence before she sees me. The magnetism between us no less diminished.

She hesitates before setting down her kit bag. She'll be playing directly towards me. Good.

The coin's tossed.

Trilby's serve.

Her serve hits the net. She's leaking the micro-expressions I had managed to squash through hypnosis. Doubt, frustration, self-hatred is unloading all over the court.

With every hit, she pushes out an animal grunt. I've never heard these noises from her. I would have stamped them out. It's a keening that comes from deep inside her. Every whine rattles my nerves like being woken by a screeching vixen in the night.

The ball flies over her head and rolls towards the backboard. It should have been an easy return.

She strikes her racket on the ground, chalk flying. Trilby swears. Code violation. Audible obscenity.

My heart tightens to watch her. She's tanking. She's giving away points with this rage.

Superbrat digs his claws into my brain. You did this. You shit. I can fix it.

Breathe, girl!

Code violation? Coaching.

"He's not with me."

The umpire shakes his head. Upholds his decision. He knows she's mine.

One more code violation and Trilby will default. She glares at me. Fire burns in her eyes. The bolt of hatred goes through me like a scalding poker.

Superbrat speaks to me with Trilby's voice. "Look at you back there. You're no one."

Whoosh!

An enthusiastic ball girl has sprung out the trap, eager to please.

It is no accident.

Trilby's racket swings up and comes down sharply across the crown of the ball girl.

A screeching gasp.

And again.

A stream of blood falls across the bronzed face of the girl. The navy uniform hides the worst of it.

Trilby stands with her weapon raised like a sword.

The inhalation from the crowd freezes my veins. I can't move. She's fucked us. I feel it again, the tightening in my chest. My eyes leave Trilby as I fold over in the grandstand.

It isn't until they're sweeping out the rubbish that anyone notices my lifeless body.

The spell is broken.

Ears open.

Hurricane of screams.

Feel blood rush tingle to ends of fingers.

A club – no – racket in my hand? Twisted wood and nylon.

See. Girl. Broken. Cowering at my feet. Red down her face. A crushed fruit.

Me. I. Did.

Population of an entire country yelling at me.

Yell back. Defend myself. Mouth. Sandpaper.

Water. Bottle bench.

People avoid my eyes as cameras zoom in. Shouting in walkie-talkies.

Missiles! Plastic cups, balled-up paper rain down from the wall
of people. Hit the girl. Protect her!

She screams when I come near.

People angrier. "Don't you dare! Get off her!"

Head, spinning full of fulness.

I see I am not I had
hotel suite
one tiny hotel
a regular tied and Trilby
I look wants me to you stop
to the hawk
I spit it keep myself entertained
All gloomy June.

Dark. Tunnel. Escape!

Not allowed to leave.

Can't come, can't go. Need to figure out what is to be done
with me.

My mind aches in the wait until -

Silent room. Air dusty hot like stepping out of an aeroplane to
an unfamiliar country.

They've taken my shoes. Laces. I'm a danger to myself.

One small window.

Ambulance with the girl in screams off. A second one. Is it for
me? No. Man loaded into the rear. Grey. Face covered.. If I
could see his eyes, I'd know for sure.

Part of me has driven away with the ambulance.

I feel lighter without it.

Breathe. Let my body respond.

Press and police don't allow me space to think. I want to speak. Holding it down suffocates me. Stuck on my tongue. Thick with anger from my heart. At myself. At him. At treasuring it all. Everything I attempt to say sounds stupid.

I speak to them with his words. Tell them what they told me. It's only in hearing it through someone else's ears does the strangeness hit me.

> *A deep breath and stroking her palm with a finger.*

> *Franz Schubert. Piano Trio No. 2 in E-Flat Major, D. 929:11 Andante con moto*

It's getting better. Sponsorship stripped. Fines tear my finances apart. I'm left with just enough to exile myself. A cottage on the coast where the crashing waves drown out his voice in my mind.

Viv gets it. Subject X. She's an unexpected friend. She's an advocate for the benefit of talking. And talking helps. Thank you for listening.

She's always - "Exorcise it. Disinfect with sunlight."

How could his influence change everything without seeming to change a thing? Magic, but magic doesn't exist. Only nature. And nature is mental.

There are these ants in the jungle, right. Millions of them, scurrying around, living happy anty lives.

But there is a fungus in the forest too. The fungus needs to separate an ant from her sisters. It unleashes a network of roots. Possesses the ant. Infiltrates ant's muscles, antennae, cute – minch minch - pinchers. Floods her with chemicals that whisper in her ear – head to the sun.

Little ant, pleased for a break from thinking about aphids, royal jelly and the hundred things demanding her attention – she only thinks sun.

This fungus moves her body up grass stalks, stems and trunk. Breaks through the canopy and all the tiny ants below. She is The Ant. Sun beaming on her.

The optimal conditions for the fungus to spore. Its fruiting body births through the skull of Little Ant. The release of pressure from ant skull –

She breathes amidst a shower of spores.

Across the treetops, other ants, twisting and changing under spores of their own. Look at them. The clear sky's bruised with burst skulls and blossoms.

Up high. With perspective. The ant knows the danger - and pleasure – of an empty head.

THE END.